START
YOUR BUSINESS
I N T E R N A T I O N A L   E D I T I O N

INTERNATIONAL LABOUR OFFICE   GENEVA

Start your business: Workbook
Geneva, International Labour Office, 2003
Management development, entrepreneur,
small scale industry, small enterprise, management. 12.04.01
ISBN 92-2-111636-0

ILO Cataloguing-in-Publication Data

Designed and typeset by Robert Silverman

Printed in Switzerland

START
YOUR BUSINESS

ABOUT START AND IMPROVE YOUR BUSINESS

Start Your Business (SYB) is an integral part of the ILO's Start and Improve Your Business (SIYB) package. SIYB is a system of interrelated training packages and support materials for small-scale entrepreneurs with limited previous exposure to management training. It is part of the InFocus Programme on Boosting Employment through Small Enterprise Development (IFP/SEED). IFP/SEED strives to assist member countries in their efforts to meet the employment challenge by creating sustainable quality jobs in the small-scale private enterprise sector. At a time when the employment capacities of the agricultural, public and large enterprise sectors cannot absorb the growing numbers in the labour market in many countries, it is clear that most future jobs will be created in the small enterprise sector.

The SIYB programme was designed to provide a sustainable and cost effective method to reach substantial numbers of small-scale entrepreneurs and provide them with the practical management skills needed in a competitive environment for profitability and growth. The programme provides individuals and institutions with a comprehensive set of materials, aimed at different segments of the small enterprise sector. It deals with various topics related to small enterprise development, such as training, business counselling, monitoring and evaluation and networking. Small enterprise development institutions and private trainers in more than 80 countries have used the SIYB programme. More information about how ILO can assist with the adaptation and implementation of the SIYB programme can be obtained from any local ILO office or from:

International Labour Office
InFocus Programme Boosting Employment through Small Enterprise Development
CH-1211 Geneva 22
Switzerland
Fax No. +41 22 799 7978
Email: ifpseed@ilo.org
Website: http://www.ilo.org/seed

At a time when the public and the large-scale enterprise sectors' capabilities to create new jobs fall short of the need for productive and fruitful employment, it is clear that most future jobs will be created in the small-scale enterprises.

Few business management publications are simple enough to be easily understood by people who have not been exposed to business training. Even fewer are practical enough to assist potential entrepreneurs through the demanding process of starting a small enterprise, especially if this is their first attempt. This book is an attempt to fill the gap.

The underlying idea is that there are clear steps that need to be followed by an entrepreneur in the process of starting a small enterprise. By following these steps the entrepreneur will maximize the chances of starting a viable and sustainable small-scale business.

SIYB is a system of interrelated training packages and support materials for small-scale entrepreneurs with limited previous exposure to management training. The programme provides individuals and institutions with a comprehensive set of materials, aimed at different segments of the small enterprise sector. It deals with various topics related to small enterprise development, such as training, business counselling, monitoring and evaluation and networking. Small enterprise development institutions and private trainers in more than 80 countries have used the SIYB programme.

This book is an integral part of the "Start and Improve Your Business" (SIYB) programme which in turn is part of the ILO's InFocus Programme on Boosting Employment through Small Enterprise Development. The SIYB programme was designed to provide a sustainable and cost effective method to reach substantial numbers of small-scale entrepreneurs and provide them with the practical management skills needed for profitability and growth in a competitive environment. The SIYB programme is progressively including principles of social responsibility in its business management training, thereby contributing to the enhancement of job quality in line with core ILO values.

This book is supplemented by a Trainer's Guide and the SIYB Business Game. The Trainer's Guide assists trainers to conduct SYB training using this book. The SIYB Game is an effective and dynamic learning tool that brings the learning points in the training programme to life.

Credit is due to the author of the original Fiji version, Geoffrey Meredith; to Douglas Stevenson, Håkan Jarskog, Barbara Murray and Ulf Kallstig who worked on the Harare edition; and finally to Klaus Haftendorn who made many inputs into the current edition.

For more information about how the ILO can assist with the adaptation of this book or the implementation of the SIYB programme in general, please contact any local ILO office or:

International Labour Office
InFocus Programme Boosting Employment through Small Enterprise Development
CH-1211 Geneva 22
Switzerland
Fax No. +41 22 799 7978
Email: ifpseed@ilo.org
Website: http://www.ilo. org/seed

Christine Evans-Klock, Director

InFocus Programme on Boosting Employment through Small Enterprise Development

CONTENTS

continued

CONTENTS
continued

INTRODUCTION

THIS CHAPTER EXPLAINS

■ The Test Yourself Exercises

■ Business Activities

The Start Your Business (SYB) programme is designed to help people who want to start their own business.

The SYB materials come in three parts:

- a Handbook that provides you with the information you need to complete the 9 SYB Steps
- the companion Workbook, which you are now reading, and
- the Business Plan

This Workbook contains two types of activity:

- Test Yourself Exercises that will help you to understand the information you read about in the SYB Handbook. Each exercise enables you to put into practice what you have learnt. If you have problems with an exercise read through the relevant text in the Handbook again. Then do the exercise again. Use a pencil to do the exercises so that the changes are easy to make. When you get an exercise wrong make sure you understand why the correct answer is different. Answers to the Test Yourself Exercises are at the back of the Workbook. Complete each exercise before checking the answer so that you have the full benefit of testing your own understanding.

- Business Activities that require you to collect and analyze information as part of the planning for your own proposed business. These activities are practical and realistic. To complete them you may have to do field work such as talking to other entrepreneurs, business people, consultants, banks, government agencies, getting prices from suppliers, asking your potential customers questions and so on. Directions are given for each activity as necessary. You record the results of your Business Activities in the forms provided in this SYB Workbook. Use a pencil until you are sure of your activities and your decisions.

You should complete all of the exercises and activities in this SYB Workbook as they will help you to:

- understand the ideas in the SYB Handbook

- make practical plans for your new business

- find out if your plans have weaknesses

- assess whether your business idea can succeed

- and prepare you to complete your own Business Plan.

Note: Since this book is intended for use in many different countries, we have used the term 'NU' in the examples to represent an imaginary 'National Unit of currency'.

TEST YOURSELF EXERCISES

The following **Test Yourself Exercises** will help you to understand the information you read about in the SYB Handbook.

Each exercise enables you to put into practice what you have learnt. If you have problems with an exercise read through the relevant text in the Handbook again. Then do the exercise again.

Use a pencil so that changes are easy to make.

NOTE: Since this book is intended for use in many different countries, we have used the term "NU" in the examples to represent an imaginary "National Unit of currency"

EXERCISE NUMBER 1   PERSONAL CASH FLOW PLAN

A person is planning to start a business. He has NU750 in cash and NU1,250 in a bank account. He has no job which means that there will be no money coming in until his planned business can pay him a salary. To support himself and his family, he needs NU200 per month. He plans to start his business in one month and after two months in business, he estimates that he will be able to draw NU400 per month in salary.

Prepare a Personal Cash Flow Plan, starting from now until his planned business will be able to support him and his family. Use the form below.

PERSONAL CASH FLOW PLAN			
A	Money available now		_____
B	Money in during next____months	+	_____
C	Total money available (A+B)	=	_____
D	Money out during next 5 months	−	_____
E	Money to invest in the business (C−D)	=	_____

The answer is on page 60 of this Workbook. When you have completed this exercise correctly, turn back to page 11 in your SYB Handbook

Are the following businesses retail, manufacturing, wholesale or service businesses?

Tick the relevant box.

	retail business	manu-facturing business	wholesale business	service business
A person who does motor vehicle repairs has a	❏	❏	❏	❏
A hairdresser has a	❏	❏	❏	❏
An electrician has a	❏	❏	❏	❏
A person who does computer repairs has a	❏	❏	❏	❏
A shoe shop is a	❏	❏	❏	❏
A furniture factory is a	❏	❏	❏	❏
A person who buys large quantities of chairs from the furniture factory and sells to other businesses has a	❏	❏	❏	❏

The answers are on page 60 of this Workbook. When you have completed this exercise correctly, turn back to page 15 in your SYB Handbook

Describe at least two reasons why customers would buy the following products or services.

Complete the following sentences.

A customer would buy:

a sun hat _____

_____

a wallet _____

_____

a typewriter repair service _____

_____

a motor vehicle service _____

_____

roofing materials _____

_____

fresh fish _____

_____

shoes _____

_____

dinner plates _____

_____

welding equipment _____

_____

a wedding dress/suit _____

_____

ANSWER

The answers are on page 61 of this Workbook. When you have completed this exercise, turn back to page 23 in your SYB Handbook

You want to open a hardware store in a village that serves as a business centre for the surrounding small farms. The area is prosperous but it is still a rural area with only gravel roads and the electricity supply is not reliable. Many of the farmers in the area do not have electricity.

Based on this information, decide what products you are going to sell in your hardware store. Tick Yes or No for each product in the list below.

	Yes	No
Fertilizer	❏	❏
Paraffin lamps	❏	❏
Gas fridges	❏	❏
Sleeping bags	❏	❏
Electric drills	❏	❏
Torches	❏	❏
Nails	❏	❏
Hammers	❏	❏
Roller skates	❏	❏
Paint	❏	❏

The answers are on page 61 of this Workbook. When you have completed this exercise correctly, turn back to page 26 in your SYB Handbook

Read through each paragraph below which describes a business.

Tick the price you would choose for the products the businesses want to sell.

1. You own a book shop, with several competitors nearby. The shop has an exclusive profile. The quality of products you sell is very good and your prices are high. Some customers have been asking for better quality pens so you are going to start selling a brand of ballpoint pen that is better than the pens your competitors sell. The competitors charge NU30–NU35 for their pens. Your costing tells you that the total cost of this particular pen is NU20. What price would you choose for your high quality pens?

   ☐ NU29.99   ☐ NU35.00   ☐ NU39.99

2. You are running a take-away restaurant in an industrial area where factory workers need to buy lunch. There are no other restaurants in the area but some customers find it too expensive to eat at your restaurant and bring packed lunches from home instead. A cheese sandwich made at home costs about NU3.00. Your restaurant's total cost of making a cheese sandwich is NU2.60. What price would you charge for a cheese sandwich?

   ☐ NU2.75   ☐ NU3.75   ☐ NU6.75

3. You are running a small brick-making industry. Your customers are mostly small construction companies. Your bricks are slightly lower quality than your large scale competitors, but some customers prefer your bricks as they are cheaper. Your competitors' price for bricks of slightly higher quality is NU0.5-NU0.55 each. Your total cost of making one brick is NU0.35. Select your price for one brick.

   ☐ NU0.35   ☐ NU0.45   ☐ NU0.55

4. You are running a men's hair salon in a good location in the shopping district of a big town. Your customers want a good haircut but do not want to pay too much for it. The exclusive hair salons in town charge between NU50 and NU80 for a haircut, and the very cheap salons charge NU10-NU15. Your total cost for a normal haircut is NU13. Choose the price for a normal haircut at your salon.

   ☐ NU15.00   ☐ NU25.00   ☐ NU50.00

The answers are on page 62 of this Workbook. When you have completed this exercise, turn back to page 27 in your SYB Handbook

Choosing the right method of distribution for products is an important decision for manufacturers. Which type of distribution would you suggest for the businesses described below? You can select more than one type of distribution for each business.

Tick the relevant box or boxes.

	Direct distribution	Retail distribution	Wholesale distribution
A tailor making clothes to order	❑	❑	❑
A large manufacturer of nails	❑	❑	❑
A local small manufacturer of sweets	❑	❑	❑
A pottery making exclusive handmade products	❑	❑	❑
A manufacturer of shampoo	❑	❑	❑
A small bakery in a residential area	❑	❑	❑
A small manufacturer of cooking pots	❑	❑	❑
A carpenter making furniture to order	❑	❑	❑

The answers are on page 62 of this Workbook. When you have completed this exercise, turn back to page 29 in your SYB Handbook

Suggest at least two ways of advertising that you think would be most suitable for each of the businesses below. Be as specific as you can and give reasons for your choices.

Advertising methods for:

A signwriter   1._____

2._____

3._____

An electrician   1._____

2._____

3._____

A general store   1._____

2._____

3._____

A restaurant   1._____

2._____

3._____

A shoe-making factory   1._____

2._____

3._____

The answers are on page 63 of this Workbook. When you have completed this exercise, turn back to page 30 in your SYB Handbook

An owner who is also the manager of a small furniture-making enterprise wants to restructure her business. Working in the business, she has three full-time carpenters, two trainees, a secretary and a salesperson. The owner would like to have two of the carpenters and one of the trainees working on making furniture and the other carpenter and trainee working on furniture repairs.

If you have disability- or mobility-related requirements, you may need people to assist you with some specific activities. Such person/s may need to be included in your organizational structure.

In the space below, draw a diagram of the organizational structure for your business.

The answers are on page 63 of this Workbook. When you have completed this exercise, turn back to page 37 in your SYB Handbook

Classify the following business costs as being either direct or indirect costs.

Tick in the appropriate box.

	Direct cost	Indirect cost
Telephone charges in a bicycle repair business	❏	❏
Spare parts to repair engines in a garage	❏	❏
Steel for a factory that makes gates	❏	❏
Wages paid to workers who make tables in a furniture factory	❏	❏
Cloth used in a dressmaking business	❏	❏
Wages paid to the business owner of a hardware store	❏	❏
Scissors used at a hairdressing salon	❏	❏
Books for sale in a book shop	❏	❏
Wages of a salesperson in a shoe shop	❏	❏
Rent of a building for a factory	❏	❏
Secretary's wages	❏	❏
Interest for a loan	❏	❏

ANSWER

The answer is on page 64 of this Workbook. When you have completed this exercise correctly, turn back to page 50 in your SYB Handbook

An entrepreneur is planning to set up a small factory. From her Cash Flow Plan she finds that she will need enough money to pay for all the business costs during the first three months of trading.

Using the form below, calculate the amount of start-up capital the entrepreneur will need to cover her operating expenses for three months.

BUSINESS START-UP OPERATING PAYMENTS

	Estimated monthly operating expenses	Operating expenses for the first three months
Rent of business premises	NU 2 000	_____
Purchase of stock	NU 1 512	_____
Insurance	NU 15	_____
Electricity	NU 45	_____
Telephone	NU 35	_____
Office supplies, paper, etc.	NU 35	_____
Promotion and advertising	NU 555	_____
Loan repayment	NU 75	_____
Owner's salary	NU 250	_____
Staff wages	NU 375	_____
TOTAL	_____	_____

The answers are on page 64 of this Workbook. When you have completed this exercise correctly, turn back to page 55 in your SYB Handbook

A business starter wants to open a printing shop. For investment and working capital he calculates that he needs NU35,000. He has NU7,000 from his own savings. The family is able to lend him NU6,000 for 3 years but they want half of the money back after the second year. The family members ask 5% interest to be proportionally paid back every 6 months.

The business starter can get the remaining NU22,000 from the local development bank on the following conditions:

Loan period:	5 years
Pay-back conditions:	yearly
Grace period:	1 year
Interest rate:	10%

What will the debt service be?

Use the form below to make your calculations.

DEBT SERVICE

6-monthly periods	1	2	3	4	5	6	7	8	9	10
FAMILY LOAN										
Instalment										
Interest										
BANK LOAN										
Instalment										
Interest										
DEBT SERVICE										
Instalment										
Interest										
TOTAL										

The answers are on page 65 of this Workbook. When you have completed this exercise correctly, turn back to page 61 in your SYB Handbook

The entrepreneur who plans to set up a retail business is estimating her cash flow for the first four months in business.

- She plans to start the business with NU40,000.
- She expects to sell for NU10,000 per month, but NU3,000 per month of these sales will be credit sales to be paid three months later.
- Salaries will be NU5,000 per month.
- Stock will be bought for NU6,000 the first month and NU2,000 each of the following two months.
- Advertising will be NU3,000 the first month and NU1,000 each of the following months.
- Payments for other costs will be NU1,000 per month.
- She will buy equipment for NU7,000 during the first month.

Use the form to make a Cash Flow Plan for the first four months for this retail business.

CASH FLOW PLAN				
	Month			
	1	2	3	4
1 Cash at the beginning of the month				
2 Cash in from sales				
3 Any other cash in				
4 TOTAL CASH IN				
5 Cash out for staff costs				
6 Cash out for operation costs				
7 Any other cash out				
8 TOTAL CASH OUT				
9 Cash at the end of the month				

The answers are on page 65 of this Workbook. When you have completed this exercise correctly, turn back to page 74 in your SYB Handbook

Consider the Cash Flow Plan for Star Bakery on page 74 of your SYB Handbook and answer the following questions:

1. What is the amount of cash coming into the business in the month of April?

    _____

2. What is the total amount of cash going out of the business in the month of May?

    _____

3. In what month does the entrepreneur expect to buy new equipment?

    _____

4. In what month does the entrepreneur expect production to increase?

    _____

5. Calculate the cash flow of Star Bakery with an initial working capital of 50% of the costs of the first month.

    a) What will be the cash situation of the Bakery?

    _____

    _____

    b) What will be the consequence for raw material purchase?

    _____

    _____

The answers are on page 66 of this Workbook. When you have completed this exercise correctly, turn back to page 75 in your SYB Handbook

Select the legal form of business you would prefer for the businesses described below.

Tick the relevant box.

	Sole proprietor	Partnership	Limited company
1. A person plans to start a shoe repair shop in his own home. He will not have any employees and he does not need to borrow money to buy tools.	❏	❏	❏
2. A group of people plan to start a factory making decorative wall tiles. A few of the owners will work in the business, others will only invest money. They will need a substantial loan from the bank to build and equip the factory.	❏	❏	❏
3. Two people plan to start a small general store together. They will both work in the store. To start the business, they will need a small loan.	❏	❏	❏
4. A builder plans to start his own construction company. He will invest a lot of capital in tools and equipment and he will employ 25 people from the start. To find capital for his business he has met a person who is willing to invest in his business if made a partner, which the entrepreneur has agreed to. He will also need a bank loan.	❏	❏	❏
5. A person plans to start a fabric weaving business in cheap rented premises. She will have a couple of employees to start with. She has most of the capital, but she will need a small loan.	❏	❏	❏

ANSWER

The answers are on page 67 of this Workbook. When you have completed this exercise, turn back to page 85 in your SYB Handbook

BUSINESS ACTIVITIES

The following **Business Activities** are provided to help you gather all the facts and information you need to start your own business.

Depending on the type of business you want to start, you may need to modify the forms or add extra pages.

Use a pencil so that changes are easy to make.

NOTE: Since this book is intended for use in many different countries, we have used the term "NU" in the examples to represent an imaginary "National Unit of currency"

BUSINESS ACTIVITY 1   PERSONAL ASSESSMENT FORM

 When you have read pages 6 - 7 in your SYB Handbook complete the form below.

- Carefully consider each of the skills, personal characteristics or situations listed. Make any relevant notes in the space provided.
- Rate each one as being either a personal strength or weakness. Be honest in your assessment.
- Explain to a close friend or family member that you are considering starting a business. Ask them to complete the form about you.
- Count your total score of strengths and weaknesses.

	Your assessment		Friend or family member's assessment	
PERSONAL CHARACTERISTICS SITUATION	STRENGTH	WEAKNESS	STRENGTH	WEAKNESS
COMMITMENT	☐	☐	☐	☐
To succeed in business you must be committed to running your business. Commitment means that you are willing to put your business before almost everything else. If you want to stay in business for a long time and you are willing to risk your own money on the business, your commitment is a strength; if you have many other priorities and do not want to spend most of your time and money on the business, this is a weakness.				
MOTIVATION	☐	☐	☐	☐
Why do you plan to start your own business? You are more likely to succeed as an entrepreneur if you plan to start because you want to try your business idea, you want to be your own boss and you want to have your own business. If you plan to start a business because you have to, for example if you are unemployed, your chances of success are generally not as good. If you are very keen to start your own business this is a strength; if you are not yet very sure but think it might be a possibility, this is a weakness.				
TAKING RISKS	☐	☐	☐	☐
There are no absolutely safe business ideas. You always run the risk of failing in your business. Although an entrepreneur must be willing to take some risks, you should only take reasonable risks. To be willing to take moderate risks is a strength; risking everything on a gamble, or not being prepared to take any risks at all, is a weakness.				
MAKING DECISIONS	☐	☐	☐	☐
In your own business, you will have to make important decisions. They cannot be passed onto someone else to make or not made at all. To be able to make difficult decisions that could have serious consequences is a strength; if you often find it difficult to decide what to do and prefer other people to tell you what to do, this is a weakness.				
FAMILY SITUATION	☐	☐	☐	☐
Running your own business will take a lot of your time. It is important to have your family's support. Your family should agree with your plans to start a business. Maybe they can even be involved and help in the business. To have a supportive family is a strength; if you do not have your family's support, this is a weakness.				
FINANCIAL SITUATION	☐	☐	☐	☐
If you have personal funds to put into your business and if it does not mean a catastrophe for your personal finances if the business fails, it is a strength. If you have no funds of your own to put into the business and if you are completely dependent on the success of your business, it is a weakness.				

	Your assessment		Friend or family member's assessment	
	STRENGTH	WEAKNESS	STRENGTH	WEAKNESS

SKILLS

TECHNICAL SKILLS
| ❑ | ❑ | ❑ | ❑ |

Technical skills are the practical abilities you need to produce the product or provide the service of your business. For example, to start a dressmaking business you need to be able to cut and sew; to start a garage you need to be able to fix engines. Before you started the SYB programme you should have had an idea for a business. If you do not have the technical skills you need for this type of business, rate this as a weakness.

BUSINESS MANAGEMENT SKILLS
| ❑ | ❑ | ❑ | ❑ |

Business management skills are the abilities you need to run your business efficiently. Marketing skills are perhaps the most important, but other skills in business management are also vital for the success of your business, for example costing and record-keeping. If you do not have these skills, this is a weakness.

KNOWLEDGE OF YOUR LINE OF BUSINESS
| ❑ | ❑ | ❑ | ❑ |

Knowledge of the specific line of business you want to start is necessary in some lines of business, in others it might not be one of the most important factors, but it will always help. If you have this experience with the type of business you want to start, this is a strength.

Count the number of strengths and the number of weaknesses you have and write the numbers here.

Compare the total number of strength ratings to the number of weakness ratings. Do you think you have enough of the necessary characteristics and skills to start your own business?

❑ YES   ❑ NO

When you have completed Business Activity 1 turn to page 8 in your SYB Handbook.

BUSINESS ACTIVITIES

When you have read page 8 of your SYB Handbook use this form to plan what you will do to improve your personal qualities as an entrepreneur.

- In the first column, list each skill, personal characteristic or situation that you identify as being a weakness.
- In the second column describe how you intend to overcome each weakness. Make sure your plans to improve your skills and characteristics are practical.

WEAK SKILL OR CHARACTERISTIC	WHAT I WILL DO TO STRENGTHEN THIS WEAKNESS

When you have completed Business Activity 2 turn to page 11 in your SYB Handbook.

When you have read through pages 9 - 11 of your SYB Handbook and completed Test Yourself Exercise Number 1, assess your own personal cash flow to estimate how much money you can invest in your planned business.

- Estimate how much money will need to come in before your new business can support you.
- Estimate how much money you will have to pay out before your new business can support you.
- Deduct the money going out from the money coming in to find out how much money you can invest in your business.

PERSONAL CASH FLOW PLAN

A	Money available now		_____
B	Money in during next____months	+	_____
		+	_____
		+	_____
C	Total money available (A+B)	=	_____
D	Money out during next 5 months	−	_____
		−	_____
		−	_____
		−	_____
		−	_____
E	Money to invest in the business (C-D)	=	_____

When you have completed Business Activity 3 turn to page 11 in your SYB Handbook and continue.

When you have read through pages 14 - 15 of your SYB Handbook use this form to describe the business you want to start.

• Think clearly and in detail about the kind of business you want to start.
• If you are not sure of the answers leave the space blank and come back later and complete it.

Name of business: _____

What type of business will it be? The business is going to be:

❑ a manufacturing business

❑ a service business

❑ a retail business

❑ a wholesale business

What products or services is the business going to deal with? The business is going to (write on the appropriate line):

❑ make the following products _____

_____

_____

_____

❑ provide the following products or services_____

_____

_____

_____

❑ run the following type of shop _____

_____

_____

_____

❑ run the following type of wholesale business _____

_____

_____

_____

Who is going to buy your products or services? The customers will be: _____

_____

_____

_____

Why will customers buy your products or services? The business will satisfy the following needs of the customers:

_____

_____

_____

_____

How is your business going to sell its products or services? The business will sell in the following way: _____

_____

_____

_____

Are there any other special points about your business? The business will: _____

_____

_____

_____

When you have completed Business Activity 4 turn to page 16 in your SYB Handbook and continue.

BUSINESS ACTIVITIES

When you have read through pages 22 - 23 of your SYB Handbook use this form to describe the customers for your business.

- Look again at your business idea summary and think about your customers.
- Visit some businesses that sell the same or similar products or services to those you want to sell and look at the types of customers.
- Ask the customers and the business owner questions which will help you to complete the form below.
* If you have many products you may need extra pages. You can describe the customers for a range of products as one group.

CUSTOMERS FOR THE BUSINESS

Product/service 1 or range of products_____

C H A R A C T E R I S T I C S

WHO WILL YOUR CUSTOMERS BE?

❑ individuals   ❑ families   ❑ other businesses   ❑ domestic use   ❑ work-related

AGE

❑ adults   ❑ elderly   ❑ teenagers   ❑ parents of children

GENDER

❑ mostly female   ❑ mostly male   ❑ both

LOCATION: THEY LIVE/WORK…

❑ nearby   ❑ at some distance

INCOME LEVELS

❑ high   ❑ medium   ❑ low

NUMBER OF CUSTOMERS_____

WHEN WILL THEY BUY THIS PRODUCT OR SERVICE

❑ daily   ❑ weekly   ❑ monthly   ❑ once per year   ❑ seasonally

HOW MUCH WILL CUSTOMERS BUY

❑ large quantities   ❑ one item regularly

FUTURE SIZE OF MARKET: IN THE FUTURE THE NUMBER OF CUSTOMERS WILL…

❑ increase   ❑ decrease   ❑ stay the same

WHY DO CUSTOMERS NEED THIS PRODUCT OR SERVICE?_____

_____

QUALITIES WANTED BY THE CUSTOMERS

❑ size   ❑ colour   ❑ price   ❑ particular features

CUSTOMERS FOR THE BUSINESS

Product/service 2 or range of products_____

C H A R A C T E R I S T I C S

WHO WILL YOUR CUSTOMERS BE?

❏ individuals   ❏ families   ❏ other businesses   ❏ domestic use   ❏ work-related

AGE

❏ adults   ❏ elderly   ❏ teenagers   ❏ parents of children

GENDER

❏ mostly female   ❏ mostly male   ❏ both

LOCATION: THEY LIVE/WORK...

❏ nearby   ❏ at some distance

INCOME LEVELS

❏ high   ❏ medium   ❏ low

NUMBER OF CUSTOMERS_____

WHEN WILL THEY BUY THIS PRODUCT OR SERVICE

❏ daily   ❏ weekly   ❏ monthly   ❏ once per year   ❏ seasonally

HOW MUCH WILL CUSTOMERS BUY

❏ large quantities   ❏ one item regularly

FUTURE SIZE OF MARKET: IN THE FUTURE THE NUMBER OF CUSTOMERS WILL...

❏ increase   ❏ decrease   ❏ stay the same

WHY DO CUSTOMERS NEED THIS PRODUCT OR SERVICE?_____

_____

QUALITIES WANTED BY THE CUSTOMERS

❏ size   ❏ colour   ❏ price   ❏ particular features

CUSTOMERS FOR THE BUSINESS

Product/service 3 or range of products_____

C H A R A C T E R I S T I C S

WHO WILL YOUR CUSTOMERS BE?

❏ individuals ❏ families ❏ other businesses ❏ domestic use ❏ work-related

AGE

❏ adults ❏ elderly ❏ teenagers ❏ parents of children

GENDER

❏ mostly female ❏ mostly male ❏ both

LOCATION: THEY LIVE/WORK…

❏ nearby ❏ at some distance

INCOME LEVELS

❏ high ❏ medium ❏ low

NUMBER OF CUSTOMERS_____

WHEN WILL THEY BUY THIS PRODUCT OR SERVICE

❏ daily ❏ weekly ❏ monthly ❏ once per year ❏ seasonally

HOW MUCH WILL CUSTOMERS BUY

❏ large quantities ❏ one item regularly

FUTURE SIZE OF MARKET: IN THE FUTURE THE NUMBER OF CUSTOMERS WILL…

❏ increase ❏ decrease ❏ stay the same

WHY DO CUSTOMERS NEED THIS PRODUCT OR SERVICE?_____

_____

QUALITIES WANTED BY THE CUSTOMERS

❏ size ❏ colour ❏ price ❏ particular features

When you have completed Business Activity 5 turn to page 24 in your SYB Handbook and continue.

When you have read through page 24 of your SYB Handbook use this form to describe the competitors for your business.

- Identify three or more existing businesses that will be competitors to your business.
- Visit their businesses and gather information.
- For each of these competitors, briefly describe each of the characteristics that are listed in the first column.

COMPETITOR CHARACTERISTICS

	COMPETITORS		
	A	B	C
Name			
Type of products or services			
Prices			
Quality of goods or services			
Equipment			
Staff skills/pay			
Location			
Distribution used			
Promotion/advertising used			
Customer services			
Other			

My competitors' major strengths are: _____

_____

_____

My competitors' major weaknesses are: _____

_____

_____

I can use this information to improve my business idea in the following ways: _____

_____

_____

Go back to Business Activity 4 on pages 24 - 25 and make any changes to your business idea that will help you compete better with similar businesses.

When you have completed Business Activity 6 turn to page 24 in your SYB Handbook and continue.

When you have read through pages 24 - 26 of your SYB Handbook use this form to describe the products or services your business will sell.

- List all the products, services or ranges of products you will sell through your business. If you have more than two (2) products, services or ranges of products, use the next page as well and add more pages.
- Describe the characteristics of each product or service or ranges of products.
- When a characteristic is not relevant to your products or services, write N/A (not applicable).

PRODUCT, SERVICES OR RANGE OF PRODUCTS

	1.	2.
General description		
Quality		
Colour		
Size		
Packaging		
Delivery		
Instruction manual		
Spare parts		
Repairs		
Other features:		

PRODUCT, SERVICES OR RANGE OF PRODUCTS

	3.	4.
General description		
Quality		
Colour		
Size		
Packaging		
Delivery		
Instruction manual		
Spare parts		
Repairs		
Other features:		

CONTINUE

When you have completed Business Activity 7 turn to page 27 in your SYB Handbook and continue.

When you have read through page 27 of your SYB Handbook use this form to describe the prices of the products or services your business will sell.

- List all the products, services or range of products you will sell through your business across the top of the form below. If you have more than four (4) products, services or ranges of products, add more pages.
- Describe the details that apply to each product or service or range of products. Use the information you collected for your customers' and competitors' profiles.
- At this stage you will not be able to estimate your costs. Later in SYB Step 5 you will estimate your production and other costs and in SYB Step 7 you can see if your turnover is higher than your costs.

PRODUCT, SERVICES OR RANGE OF PRODUCTS

	1.	2.

DETAILS

Competitors' prices

- highest _____ _____

- average _____ _____

- lowest _____ _____

My estimated price _____ _____

Reason for setting price _____ _____

Discounts will be given to the
following types of customers _____ _____

Reason for discounts _____ _____

Credit will be given to the
following types of customers _____ _____

Reason for credit _____ _____

Ideas for special prices to increase sales such as special offers, month-end reductions, bulk orders etc.:

_____

_____

_____

_____

PRODUCT, SERVICES OR RANGE OF PRODUCTS

	3.	4.

DETAILS

Competitors' prices

  • highest

  _____ _____

  • average

  _____ _____

  • lowest

  _____ _____

My estimated price

  _____ _____

Reason for setting price

  _____ _____

Discounts will be given to the
following types of customers

  _____ _____

Reason for discounts

  _____ _____

Credit will be given to the
following types of customers

  _____ _____

Reason for credit

  _____ _____

Ideas for special prices to increase sales such as special offers, month-end reductions, bulk orders etc.:

_____

_____

_____

_____

CONTINUE

*When you have completed Business Activity 8 turn to page 28 in your
SYB Handbook and continue.*

When you have read through pages 28 -29 of your SYB Handbook use this form to describe the location and distribution method of your business.

- Visit your competitors' businesses and think about their locations and methods of distribution.
- Talk to your potential customers and suppliers.
- Get information about the costs of buying or renting various premises or vehicles, etc.
- Decide which location or method of distribution will suit your business, then fill in this form.

The business will be located at:

_____

_____

_____

My reasons for choosing this location are:

_____

_____

_____

METHOD OF DISTRIBUTION *(tick all that are relevant to your business idea)*

To get my products or services to my customers I will:

❑ sell direct from my shop/factory/warehouse/office/home (delete those not applicable)

❑ sell to retailers/other shops

❑ deliver

❑ sell to wholesalers

❑ sell door-to-door/on the street

❑ take orders by phone

❑ other (describe) _____

_____

_____

My reasons for choosing this form of distribution:

_____

_____

_____

When you have completed Business Activity 9 turn to page 30 in your SYB Handbook and continue.

When you have read through page 30 of your SYB Handbook use this form to describe the kinds of promotion you will use for your business.

- Visit your competitors and think about the types of promotion they use. Make a list.
- Find out about the costs of different types of advertising such as advertisements in newspapers, painted signs, printed posters, price lists, business cards or leaflets.
- Read books about promotion and decide on methods of sales promotion you can use in your business, such as displays, etc.
- Fill in the form below listing the types of promotion your business will benefit from and which you will be able to afford.

TYPE OF ADVERTISING	DESCRIBE HOW YOU WILL USE IT	COST

TYPE OF ADVERTISING	DESCRIBE HOW YOU WILL USE IT	COST

Other ideas_____

_____

_____

When you have completed Business Activity 10 turn to page 31 in your SYB Handbook and continue.

When you have read through page 31 of your SYB Handbook complete the Sales Plan form on this page.

- Fill in your estimated quantities of monthly sales of every type of goods, group of goods, or services your business expects to sell.
- Write in your selling price for every item.
- If you already plan at this stage to have a price increase during the first 12 months, indicate the new price in the appropriate column.

SALES PLAN

PJroduct/ Range of products/ Services					Month							
	1	2	3	4	5	6	7	8	9	10	11	12
1. quantity												
price/unit (in NU)												
2. quantity												
price/unit (in NU)												
3. quantity												
price/unit (in NU)												
4. quantity												
price/unit (in NU)												
5. quantity												
price/unit (in NU)												
6. quantity												
price/unit (in NU)												
7. quantity												
price/unit (in NU)												
8. quantity												
price/unit (in NU)												
9. quantity												
price/unit (in NU)												
quantity												
price/unit (in NU)												
quantity												
price/unit (in NU)												
quantity												
price/unit (in NU)												
quantity												
price/unit (in NU)												
quantity												
price/unit (in NU)												
quantity												
price/unit (in NU)												

When you have completed Business Activity 11 turn to page 32 in your SYB Handbook and continue.

When you have read through pages 34 - 36 of your SYB Handbook fill in this form giving details of the staff you will have in your business.

- Look at the tasks listed in the first column. These are the common tasks that must be done in all businesses.
- Add to this list any other specific tasks that must be done in your business to produce or provide your goods or services.
- Decide if you have the time and the necessary skills to do each of these tasks yourself.
- If you do not have the time or experience you will need to employ someone to do these tasks. Work out how many staff you will need for each task and the skills and experience they need.
- Add up the total number of employees your business will need.
- Decide if you will have partners, employ family members, and who your advisers will be.

STAFF REQUIREMENTS

TASK	SKILLS, EXPERIENCE AND OTHER REQUIREMENTS TO COMPLETE THIS TASK	DO YOU HAVE TIME AND SKILLS TO PERFORM THIS TASK?	NUMBER OF EMPLOYEES REQUIRED
General office administration	_____	❏ YES ❏ NO	_____
Record-keeping	_____	❏ YES ❏ NO	_____
Marketing and promotion	_____	❏ YES ❏ NO	_____
Costing and pricing	_____	❏ YES ❏ NO	_____
Buying products, raw materials, services, etc.	_____	❏ YES ❏ NO	_____
Supervising production	_____	❏ YES ❏ NO	_____
Production (specify tasks)	_____	❏ YES ❏ NO	_____
Selling	_____	❏ YES ❏ NO	_____
Stock control	_____	❏ YES ❏ NO	_____
Cleaning	_____	❏ YES ❏ NO	_____
Delivery	_____	❏ YES ❏ NO	_____

TASK	SKILLS, EXPERIENCE AND OTHER REQUIREMENTS TO COMPLETE THIS TASK	DO YOU HAVE TIME AND SKILLS TO PERFORM THIS TASK?	NUMBER OF EMPLOYEES REQUIRED
Other tasks (specify)	_____	❏ YES ❏ NO	_____
	_____	❏ YES ❏ NO	_____
	_____	❏ YES ❏ NO	_____
	_____	❏ YES ❏ NO	_____
	_____	❏ YES ❏ NO	_____
Total number of employees	_____	❏ YES ❏ NO	_____

continued

My business will have _____ partners. They will be: _____

._____

_____

____._____

I will employ _____ members of my family. They will be employed as: _____

._____

_____

_____

My business advisers are/will be: _____

._____

_____

_____

When you have completed Business Activity 12 turn to page 36 in your SYB Handbook and continue.

When you have read through pages 36 - 37 of your SYB Handbook decide on the organizational structure of your business.

- List the different sections (for example, administration, production, selling) in your business.
- List the number of staff in each section.
- Decide who will be in charge of each section.
- Draw a diagram showing the organizational structure for your business. Make sure that all of the staff in your business are shown in this structure.

SECTION	STAFF
_____	_____
_____	_____
_____	_____
_____	_____
_____	_____
_____	_____

The structure of my business will look like this:

When you have completed Business Activity 13 turn to page 38 in your SYB Handbook and continue.

When you have read through pages 38 - 39 of your SYB Handbook, use the equipment form below to list the equipment you will need for your business by functional units like production, storage, sales, administration, etc.

- Add technical specifications so that you can check if the machines' capacities match your production programme.
- The power connection indicates how strong your main power supply has to be.
- The price of the equipment is needed to calculate your investment and your financial needs.
- The cost of any adaptations required to equipment, machinery or premises for the entrepreneur or for employees with disability-related needs.

EQUIPMENT REQUIREMENTS

TYPE OF EQUIPMENT	SPECIFICATION	POWER CONNECTION	PRICE
TOTAL INVESTMENT			

When you have completed Business Activity 14 turn to page 40 in your SYB Handbook and continue.

When you have read through page 40, use the space below to make a drawing of how you will place your equipment.

- Take into consideration the space needed for each item of equipment and the space needed for the person who operates the equipment.
- Use a scale of 1:5 (most drawings of houses are at this scale).

When you have completed Business Activity 15 turn to page 41 in your SYB Handbook and continue.

When you have read through page 41 of your SYB Handbook, you will quantify all the production inputs your business will need.

- Make enquiries about prices. Find out where you can get the cheapest prices for good quality products for your inputs.
- Then fill in the form below using the best price you could find and the quantity you will need according to your planned sales or production plan.

INPUTS ACCORDING TO THE SALES OR PRODUCTION PLAN

		Quantity Per Month												Per Year
		Jan	Feb	Mar	Apr	May	Jun	Jul	Aug	Sep	Oct	Nov	Dec	
Production/sales														
Inputs	Price/Unit													

CONTINUE

When you have completed Business Activity 16 turn to page 42 in your SYB Handbook and continue.

When you have read through pages 44 - 45, go back to Business Activity 12 where you have identified your staff requirements and write these on the form below.

- Then find out what the usual average monthly salaries are for all the staff you need.
- Include all the social costs related to salaries like health insurance, contribution to pension funds, etc., if this is usual in your business.
- Fill in the monthly and yearly staff costs and calculate the total costs.

	STAFF REQUIREMENTS		STAFF COSTS	
NO.	DESIGNATION	QUALIFICATION	SALARY/MONTH	SALARY/YEAR
	TOTAL			

When you have completed Business Activity 17 turn to page 45 in your SYB Handbook and continue.

When you have read through pages 45 - 47 of your SYB Handbook, go back to Business Activity 16 and calculate according to the quantity of the inputs and the prices you obtained, to record the monthly costs of each input.

Use the form below to record your calculations.

MONTHLY AND YEARLY COSTS FOR BUSINESS INPUTS

	C O S T S P E R M O N T H												Per Year
	Jan	Feb	Mar	Apr	May	Jun	Jul	Aug	Sep	Oct	Nov	Dec	
Production/Sales (units)													
Cost of Inputs													
Operation costs													
Interest													
Depreciation													
TOTAL COSTS													

When you have completed Business Activity 18 turn to page 48 in your SYB Handbook and continue.

When you have read through pages 52 - 55 turn back to Business Activity 14 on page 40 and complete the form with your final choice of investment items (machines, tools, furniture, etc.) by adding the technical specifications and the best prices you could find.

- If you haven't got quotations which include transportation and installation of the machines, then add at least 5% for these costs to the price.

When you have completed Business Activity 19 turn to page 55 in your SYB Handbook and continue.

When you have completed Business Activity 19, fill the value of your investment items in the Depreciation form below.

- Estimate the period of normal use for each item and write it on the form.
- Then calculate the annual depreciation and the average monthly depreciation and record this figure in the Costs for Business Inputs form for Business Activity 18 on page 44.

DEPRECIATION

INVESTMENT ITEM	VALUE	YEARS OF USE	ANNUAL DEPRECIATION
TOTAL			

When you have completed Business Activity 20 turn to page 56 in your SYB Handbook and continue.

When you have read through pages 53 - 56 in your SYB Handbook, you can determine your working capital needs.

- Estimate how many months it will take before you can cover your expenditure for your business from your sales revenues.
- Then go to the Cost for Business Inputs form on page 44 and add up the operation costs and the staff costs for the number of estimated months. This will give you the amount of working capital you need to start your business.

WORKING CAPITAL

My business will need NU_____ working capital.

When you have completed Business Activity 21 turn to page 56 in your SYB Handbook and continue.

When you have read through pages 56 - 61 calculate the finance you need. This is the amount needed for investment and for working capital.

- Use the form below to write down the value of the different investment items necessary to run your future business.

FINANCE NEEDS	Amount (NU)
INVESTMENT	
– Land	
– Building	
– Machinery	
– Vehicle	
– Miscellaneous	
TOTAL INVESTMENT	
WORKING CAPITAL	
TOTAL FINANCE NEEDED	

When you have completed Business Activity 22 turn to page 61 in your SYB Handbook and continue.

Make a list of possible finance sources which are likely to finance your business and write them down on the bottom of your Financing Scheme form.

- Write down their loan conditions.
- Then work out a realistic financing scheme on the same form by indicating how much money you will use from which source.
- You should have at least 10% as owner's equity which comes from your own savings. If you do not have at least 10% of your own money invested in your business it will be very unlikely that you can benefit from a bank loan or governmental scheme. And if you do get a loan the financial burden caused by the credit will be too high.

FINANCING SCHEME

Finance needs

Owner's equity _____   _____

Other sources (1)

1. _____   +   _____

1. _____   +   _____

1. _____   +   _____

1. _____   +   _____

TOTAL (must be the same as required start-up capital)   =   _____

Loan conditions of the other sources

1. _____

2. _____

3. _____

4. _____

Footnote

(1) Family, friends, bank, special scheme

When you have completed Business Activity 22 turn to page 61 in your SYB Handbook and continue.

Take your Financing Scheme from Business Activity 23 and calculate the debt service (interests and instalment) for each source of financing according to their different loan conditions.

- Fill in the Debt Service form below.
- Then write the amount of interest to be paid in your Costs for Business Inputs form in Business Activity 18 on page 44.

Now you have all the elements to calculate the total costs of your future business.

DEBT SERVICE								
Instalment periods	1	2	3	4	5	6	7	8
PRIVATE LOAN Instalment								
Interest								
BANK LOAN 1 Instalment								
Interest								
BANK LOAN 2 Instalment								
Interest								
DEBT SERVICE Instalment								
Interest								
TOTAL DEBT SERVICE								

When you have completed Business Activity 23 turn to page 61 in your SYB Handbook and continue.

When you have read through pages 64 - 68 in your SYB Handbook and worked through all the previous Business Activities, you will be able to establish your Sales and Costs Plan.

- This plan will show you if your future business will make a profit or not.
- Fill in the Sales and Costs Plan on the next page by following the steps described on pages 67 - 68 of your SYB Handbook.

SALES AND COSTS PLAN

	\multicolumn{13}{c}{Per Month}
	Jan	Feb	Mar	Apr	May	Jun	Jul	Aug	Sep	Oct	Nov	Dec	Per Year
Sales													
Product 1 (quantity x price)													
Product 2 (quantity x price)													
Product 3 (quantity x price))													
Product 4 (quantity x price)													
TOTAL SALES													
COSTS													
Staff costs													
Operation costs													
Depreciation													
Interest													
TOTAL COSTS													
GROSS PROFIT													
Income Tax ___%													
NET PROFIT													

When you have completed Business Activity 24 turn to page 61 in your SYB Handbook and continue.

When you have read through pages 70 - 73 of your SYB Handbook you will know how important it is to control the money which flows in and out of your business over the year.

- Follow the directions given on pages 72 - 73 in your SYB Handbook to fill in your Cash Flow Plan.
- Cash at the start of the first month you begin your business will come from your working capital.
- When you have calculated your Cash Flow Plan you will see if the business will always have enough cash or if the business will run out of cash during the first year.
- If your Cash Flow Plan shows that the business will run out of cash, look for the reason. It may be that your working capital is too small; or your costs are too high; or you plan to give too much credit to your clients.
- To convince your family members or the loan officer of your financial institution that your business will generate enough money to support the interests and the instalments of the loan, prepare a Cash Flow Plan which covers the whole loan period.
- As you will not know whether your business will increase, decrease or remain stable, make the assumption that it remains stable. Then you can use the same sales and costs figures for the following years.

CASH FLOW PLAN

	Per Month											
	1	2	3	4	5	6	7	8	9	10	11	12
1 Cash at the beginning of the month												
2 Cash in from sales												
3 Any other cash in												
4 TOTAL CASH IN												
5 Cash out for staff costs												
6 Cash out for operation costs												
7 Any other cash out												
8 TOTAL CASH OUT												
9 Cash at the end of the month												

continued

CASH FLOW PLAN FOR THE LOAN PERIOD								
	1	2	3	4	5	6	7	8
1 Cash at the beginning of the year								
2 Cash in from sales								
3 Any other cash in								
4 TOTAL CASH IN								
5 Cash out for staff/operation costs								
6 Taxes & any other cash out								
7 TOTAL CASH OUT								
8 Debt service								
9 Cash at the end of the year								

CONTINUE

When you have completed Business Activity 26 turn to page 74 in your SYB Handbook and continue.

When you have read through pages 80 - 84 of your SYB Handbook decide on the legal form most appropriate for your business.

- Visit your competitors and find out what legal form of business they have.
- Ask business trainers, the bank and your advisers questions about the best form for your business before you make your decision.

The business will operate as a (tick only one):

❑ Sole proprietor

❑ Partnership

❑ Limited company

❑ Other (specify) _____

The reasons for choosing this type of legal form are:

a) _____

_____

_____

b) _____

_____

_____

c) _____

_____

_____

The business owners will be:

Name _____   Description of their skills and relevant experience

_____   _____

_____   _____

_____   _____

_____   _____

When you have completed Business Activity 27 turn to page 85 in your SYB Handbook and continue.

When you have read through pages 80 - 84 of your SYB Handbook decide on the legal responsibilities and insurance for your business.

- Talk to business trainers, your bank manager or other business advisers about the various specific legal responsibilities of a small business in your country.
- Visit the Ministry of Labour (or the government department that deals with labour in your country) and find out about the labour laws for your type of business.
- Visit several insurance companies and find out about the different insurance schemes they offer and the costs.
- Write down information and keep it.

LEGAL RESPONSIBILITY	APPLIES TO YOUR BUSINESS (YES OR NO)	SOURCE OF MORE INFORMATION	COST
TAXES			
Sales tax			
Employees' taxes			
Tax on business profits			
Other taxes (specify)			
EMPLOYEES			
Minimum wage			
Working hours			
Holidays			
Occupational safety & health			
Sick leave			
Other conditions (specify)			

continued

LEGAL RESPONSIBILITY	APPLIES TO YOUR BUSINESS (YES OR NO)	SOURCE OF MORE INFORMATION	COST
BUSINESS LICENCES & PERMITS			
Business licence	_____	_____	_____
Other licences, etc. (specify)	_____	_____	_____
_____	_____	_____	_____
_____	_____	_____	_____
_____	_____	_____	_____
_____	_____	_____	_____
_____	_____	_____	_____
INSURANCE			
Property	_____	_____	_____
Damage	_____	_____	_____
Medical	_____	_____	_____
Other insurance (specify)	_____	_____	_____
_____	_____	_____	_____
_____	_____	_____	_____
_____	_____	_____	_____
_____	_____	_____	_____
OTHER			
_____	_____	_____	_____
_____	_____	_____	_____
_____	_____	_____	_____
_____	_____	_____	_____
_____	_____	_____	_____

CONTINUE

When you have completed Business Activity 28 turn to page 86 in your SYB Handbook and continue.

BUSINESS ACTIVITIES

When you have completed the Business Plan for your proposed business and read pages 88 - 89 in your SYB Handbook, you can assess whether you should go ahead and start your own business.

- You need to complete this form honestly.
- Answer each of the questions by ticking either YES or NO. If you are unsure, then tick NO.
- Count up the number of NO answers.
- Use the scoring method as shown to decide on your next action.

Questions	Your Assessment	
	YES	NO
Have you decided what products or services you are going to sell?	❑	❑
Do you know who your customers will be?	❑	❑
Have you asked any potential customers what they think about your products or services?	❑	❑
Do you know who your main competitors will be?	❑	❑
Do you know what prices your competitors charge?	❑	❑
Do you know your competitors' strengths and weaknesses?	❑	❑
Have you decided what prices you will charge?	❑	❑
Have you found a business location?	❑	❑
Have you decided what type of distribution you will use?	❑	❑
Have you decided what type of promotion you will use?	❑	❑
Do you know how much your promotion will cost?	❑	❑
Have you decided which legal form is best for your business?	❑	❑
Have you decided what staff you will need?	❑	❑
Have you prepared job descriptions for your staff?	❑	❑
Do you know all the legal requirements for your business?	❑	❑
Do you know what licences your business will need?	❑	❑
Do you know how much these business licences will cost?	❑	❑
Have you decided what insurance your business will need?	❑	❑
Do you know how much the insurance will cost?	❑	❑
Have you calculated the amount of start-up capital you need to start your business?	❑	❑
Have you raised all the start-up capital for your business?	❑	❑
Have you made a Sales and Costs Plan?	❑	❑
Does your Sales and Costs Plan show a profit for the first year?	❑	❑
Have you made a Cash Flow Plan?	❑	❑
Does your Cash Flow Plan show that you will not run out of cash during the first six months of running your business?	❑	❑
Have you completed a Business Plan for your new business?	❑	❑
Have you shown your Business Plan to other people who can give advice?	❑	❑
Do you feel confident to start your business?	❑	❑
TOTAL	_____	_____

Number of NO answers	Feedback
0	You are well prepared and you can go ahead and start up your business. Your next step will be to prepare a Business Start-Up Action Plan.
1 - 10	You should go back to the SYB Steps and work on those aspects that need to be improved.
More than 10	At this stage it is too risky for you to consider starting a business. If you are still keen to start your own business you should go back and start from the beginning of the SYB programme. Maybe you need to change your business idea or get some advice from a business trainer.

When you have completed Business Activity 29 turn to page 90 in your SYB Handbook and continue.

Directions for use:

- Go back to each of the 8 SYB Steps that you have now completed and, in the form below, make a list of the activities that you have not yet finished or those that you must do before you start your business.
- Write down who will do each activity and when it will be done.

SYB STEP	ACTION THAT NEEDS TO BE CARRIED OUT	WHO WILL DO IT?	WHEN WILL IT BE DONE?
SYB Step 1 Assess yourself as an entrepreneur			
SYB Step 2 Develop your business idea			
SYB Step 3 Assess your market and develop a marketing plan			
SYB Step 4 Organize your business			
SYB Step 5 Cost your products or services			
SYB Step 6 Estimate your start-up capital			
SYB Step 7 Make financial plans			
SYB Step 8 Know your business responsibilities and choose a legal form for your business			

ANSWERS
TO THE TEST
YOURSELF
EXERCISES

Perform each exercise in the **Test Yourself Exercises** section before referring to this section.

NOTE: Since this book is intended for use in many different countries, we have used the term "NU" in the examples to represent an imaginary "National Unit of currency"

ANSWER

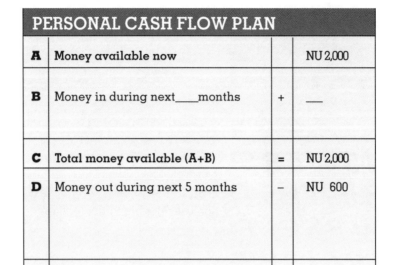

	PERSONAL CASH FLOW PLAN		
A	Money available now		NU 2,000
B	Money in during next____months	+	___
C	Total money available (A+B)	=	NU 2,000
D	Money out during next 5 months	–	NU 600
E	Money to invest in the business (C–D)	=	NU 1,400

ANSWER

	retail business	manu-facturing business	wholesale business	service business
A person who does motor vehicle repairs has a	❏	❏	❏	☑
A hairdresser has a	❏	❏	❏	☑
An electrician has a	❏	❏	❏	☑
A person who does computer repairs has a	❏	❏	❏	☑
A shoe shop is a	☑	❏	❏	❏
A furniture factory is a	❏	☑	❏	❏
A person who buys large quantities of chairs from the furniture factory and sells to other businesses has a	❏	❏	☑	❏

Here are some reasons why customers would buy the following products or services:

- *a sun hat* to enhance the face / to protect from the sun.
- *a wallet* to keep money in / to look stylish / to organize business cards.
- *a typewriter repair* to get a broken typewriter fixed / to make it work better.
- *a motor vehicle service* to maintain the car well / to fix a broken car / to make a car run more efficiently.
- *roofing materials* to repair a leaking roof / to complete a new house.
- *fresh fish* to feed the family / for a special dinner.
- *shoes* to wear to work / for their appearance / to protect the feet.
- *dinner plates* for home use / as a present for a friend / to impress the neighbours.
- *welding equipment* for fixing broken metalwork at home / for a metalworking business.
- *a wedding dress/suit* to wear at a wedding / to go to a party.

There are no definite right or wrong answers for this exercise because each entrepreneur chooses the products he or she wants to sell.

The answers below are suggestions.

	Yes	No
Fertilizer	☑	❑
Paraffin lamps	☑	❑
Gas fridges	☑	❑
Sleeping bags	❑	☑
Electric drills	❑	☑
Torches	☑	❑
Nails	☑	❑
Hammers	☑	❑
Roller skates	❑	☑
Paint	☑	❑

There are no definite right or wrong answers for this exercise but the prices you choose will affect your sales. The answers below are suggestions.

1. Your ballpoint pen is better quality than the pens your competitors sell and your shop has a more exclusive profile. For these reasons, you should probably set a price that is higher than your competitors' price of NU30.00-NU35.00

    ☐ NU29.99   ☐ NU35.00   ☑ NU39.99

2. It is reasonable to have a higher price than the cost of a homemade sandwich, which is NU3.00, but the price should only be slightly higher, or the customers will bring a packed lunch instead.

    ☐ NU2.75   ☑ NU3.75   ☐ NU6.75

3. The reason customers buy your lower quality bricks is because you sell at a cheap price, so the price must be less than your competitors' price. But your price must still be higher than your costs. Your price must be somewhere between NU0.35 and NU0.50

    ☐ NU0.35   ☑ NU0.45   ☐ NU0.55

4. You are running a medium-range hair salon and should set you price between the prices charged by the cheap salons and the exclusive ones. So your price should be between NU15.00 and NU50.00.

    ☐NU15.00   ☑ NU25.00   ☐ NU50.00

There are no definitely right or wrong answers when selecting a method of distribution. The answers below are suggestions.

	Direct distribution	Retail distribution	Wholesale distribution
A tailor making clothes to order	☑	☐	☐
A large manufacturer of nails	☐	☐	☑
A local small manufacturer of sweets	☑	☑	☐
A pottery making exclusive handmade products	☑	☑	☐
A manufacturer of shampoo	☐	☐	☑
A small bakery in a residential area	☑	☑	☐
A small manufacturer of cooking pots	☐	☑	☑
A carpenter making furniture to order	☑	☐	☐

There are no right or wrong answers for this exercise. The methods you choose to advertise your business depend on local conditions, for example the publications that are available in an area, if local radio is available, where the business is located and local customs of advertising. The following are suggestions:

A **signwriter** might best use posters and signs which will be cheap to produce and show people the sort of work he does. She might also advertise in the local newspaper.

An **electrician** could have a business card printed to give to builders, businesses and all potential clients. He could have a bright informative sign made to display outside the job he is currently doing.

A **general store** could have posters made to display in their window telling customers about special offers. They could have a leaflet printed showing pictures of their goods and their prices to give to people in the street.

A **restaurant** could send a list of the foods they offer to all the nearby businesses, factories, etc. They could advertise on radio and in the local newspaper.

A **shoe-making factory** could produce a business card and list of the types of shoes they make, the materials they use and the prices they charge, to take to retail stores. They could also have posters made to display in the stores with photographs of their shoes.

If there is any special aspect of your business which may attract customers, such as the fact that it is environmentally friendly, or that you employ people with disabilities, you can emphasize this in your advertising or in the front window of your premises.

The owner and manager of the furniture-manufacturing business could restructure her operations like this:

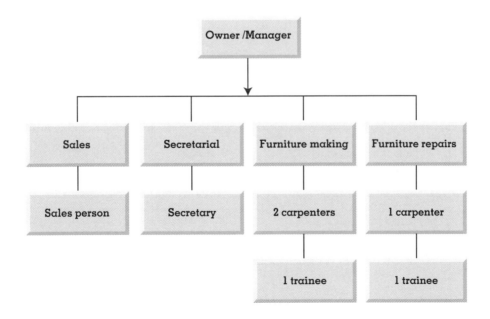

	Direct cost	Indirect cost
Telephone charges in a bicycle repair business	☐	☑
Spare parts to repair engines in a garage	☑	☐
Steel for a factory that makes gates	☑	☐
Wages paid to workers who make tables in a furniture factory	☑	☐
Cloth used in a dressmaking business	☑	☐
Wages paid to the business owner of a hardware store	☑	☐
Scissors used at a hairdressing salon	☐	☑
Books for sale in a book shop	☑	☐
Wages of a salesperson in a shoe shop	☐	☑
Rent of a building for a factory	☐	☑
Secretary's wages	☐	☑
Interest for a loan	☐	☑

The entrepreneur will need NU14,691 to cover her operating expenses for the first three months. The calculation is as follows:

BUSINESS START-UP OPERATING PAYMENTS		
	Estimated monthly operating expenses	Operating expenses for the first three months
Rent of business premises	NU 2 000	NU 6 000
Purchase of stock	NU 1 512	NU 4 536
Insurance	NU 15	NU 45
Electricity	NU 45	NU 135
Telephone	NU 35	NU 105
Office supplies, paper, etc.	NU 35	NU 105
Promotion and advertising	NU 555	NU 1 665
Loan repayment	NU 75	NU 225
Owner's salary	NU 250	NU 225
Staff wages	NU 375	NU 750
TOTAL		NU 14 691

The debt service table looks like this:

DEBT SERVICE

6 monthly periods	1	2	3	4	5	6	7	8	9	10
FAMILY LOAN	6 000	6 000	6 000	6 000	5 000	6 000	—	—	—	—
Instalment	—	—	—	3 000	—	3 000	—	—	—	—
Interest	150	150	150	150	75	75	—	—	—	—
BANK LOAN	—	22 000	—	22 000	—	16 500	—	11 000	—	5 500
Instalment	—	—	—	5 500		5 500	—	5 500	—	5 500
Interest	—	2 200	—	2 200	—	1 650	—	1 100	—	550
DEBT SERVICE										
Instalment	—	—	—	8 500	—	8 500	—	5 500	—	5 500
Interest	150	2 350	150	2 350	75	1 725	—	1 100	—	550
TOTAL	150	2 350	150	10 850	75	10 225	—	6 600	—	6 050

CASH FLOW PLAN

	Month			
	1	2	3	4
1 Cash at the beginning of the month	40 000	25 000	23 000	21 000
2 Cash in from sales	7 000	7 000	7 000	10 000
3 Any other cash in	—	—	—	—
4 TOTAL CASH IN	47 000	32 000	30 000	31 000
5 Cash out for staff costs	5 000	5 000	5 000	5 000
6 Cash out for operation costs	10 000	4 000	4 000	4 000
7 Any other cash out	7 000	—	—	—
8 TOTAL CASH OUT	22 000	9 000	9 000	9 000
9 Cash at the end of the month	25 000	23 000	21 000	19 000

ANSWER

1. The amount of cash coming into the business in the month of April is NU10,000.

2. The total amount of cash going out of the business in the month of May is NU10,475.

3. The Star Bakery does not plan to buy new equipment during the first year.

4. The owner of Star Bakery has foreseen production increase in February, March, April, May, June, July, August and in November and December.

5. Cash Flow Plan (see below)

   a) Although working capital is reduced to 50%, Star Bakery will not run out of cash. This means that Star Bakery could have started with a loan smaller than NU12,000, but not smaller than NU8,500.

   b) Cash at the end of the month does not cover the cost for the stock of raw material for the whole next month. The owner of Star Bakery has to buy the raw materials at least two times a month. The risk is that she will run out of stock if there is any supply problem and that the supplier charges higher prices for smaller quantities.

CASH FLOW PLAN

Sales						Per Month						
	Jan	Feb	Mar	Apr	May	Jun	Jul	Aug	Sep	Oct	Nov	Dec
1 Cash at the beginning of the month	3 564	2 686	2 413	2 489	2 865	3 640	4 090	5 524	7 358	9 192	10 971	13 007
2 Cash in from sales	6 250	7 500	8 750	10 000	11 250	12 500	13 750	15 000	15 000	15 000	15 625	16 250
3 Any other cash in	-	-	-	-	-	-	-	-	-	-	-	-
4 TOTAL CASH IN	9 814	10 186	11 163	12 485	14 115	16 140	17 840	20 524	22 358	24 192	26 596	29 257
5 Cash out for staff costs	4 250	5 100	5 950	6 800	7 650	8 500	9 350	10 200	10 200	10 200	10 600	11 050
6 Cash out for operation costs	2 878	2 673	2 724	2 824	2 825	3 070	2 966	2 966	966	3 021	2 989	3 007
7 Any other cash out	-	-	-	-	-	480	-	-	-	-	-	3 300
8 TOTAL CASH OUT	7 128	7 773	8 674	9 624	10 475	12 050	12 316	13 166	13 166	13 221	13 589	17 357
9 Cash at the end of the month	2 686	2 413	2 489	2 865	3 640	4 090	5 524	7 358	9 192	10 971	13 007	11 900

ANSWER

There are no definite right or wrong answers for this exercise. The answers below are suggestions:

1. A person plans to start a shoe repair shop in his own home. He will not have any employees and he does not need to borrow money to buy tools.

   Sole proprietorship is a suitable legal form for a small business operating from home with no employees and with no debts.

2. A group of people plan to start a factory making decorative wall tiles. A few of the owners will work in the business, others will only invest money. They will need a substantial loan from the bank to build and equip the factory.

   The risk in this business is big with the large bank loan and there will be owners who are not working in the business. To reduce the owners' risk and to give the owners not working in the business a formalized way of influencing the decision making and monitoring the business, a limited company is probably the most suitable legal form.

3. Two people plan to start a small general store together. They will both work in the store. To start the business, they will need a small loan.

   The risk in this business is limited, so a partnership is a suitable legal form for two partners starting a business.

4. A builder plans to start his own construction company. He will invest a lot of capital in tools and equipment and he will employ 25 people from the start. To find capital for his business he has met a person who is willing to invest in his business if made a partner, which the entrepreneur has agreed to. He will also need a bank loan.

   This business will be big and have debts. To reduce the owners' risk and to give the owner not working in the business an opportunity to influence decisions and to monitor the business, a limited company is probably the most suitable legal form of business.

5. A person plans to start a fabric weaving business in cheap rented premises. She will have a couple of employees to start with. She has most of the capital needed, but will need a small loan.

   This business will be small and the risk limited. A sole proprietorship is probably the most suitable form of business, because a limited company is rather expensive to start.

If you want to know more about how to run a business,

the ILO publication *IMPROVE YOUR BUSINESS BASICS*

will help you to improve the management

of one important part of your business. There are

six topics in the *IMPROVE YOUR BUSINESS BASICS* —

Marketing, Buying, Stock control, Costing,

Record keeping and *Financial planning.*